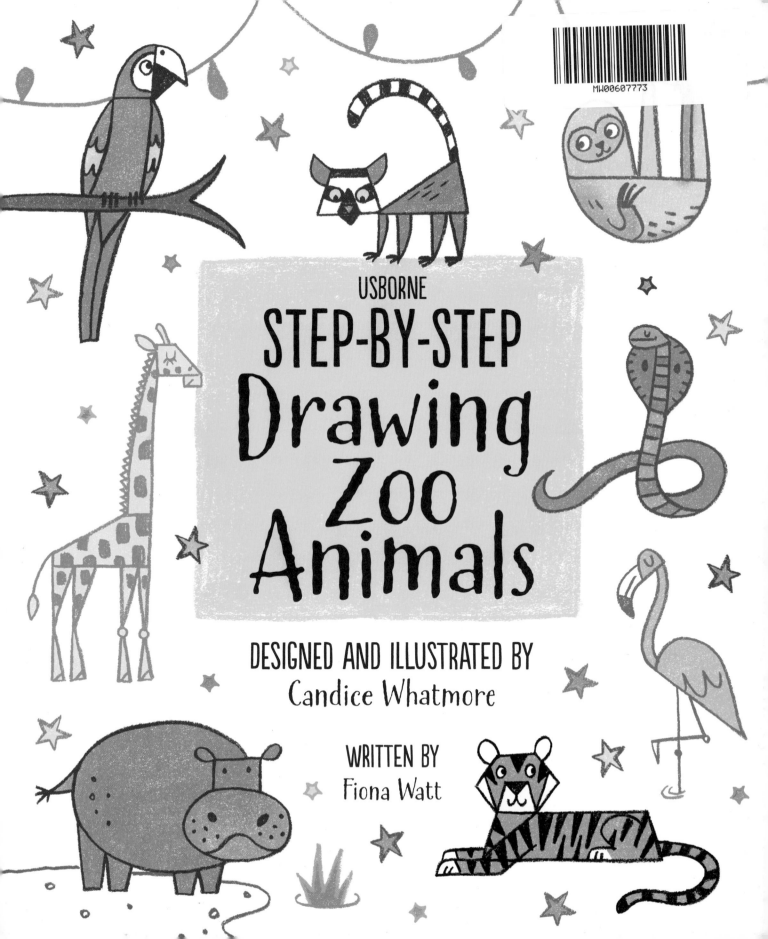

Usborne

STEP-BY-STEP
Drawing Zoo Animals

DESIGNED AND ILLUSTRATED BY
Candice Whatmore

WRITTEN BY
Fiona Watt

How to draw a lion

1. Draw a petal shape...

2. ...this shape inside...

3. ...a body...

Your turn...

2

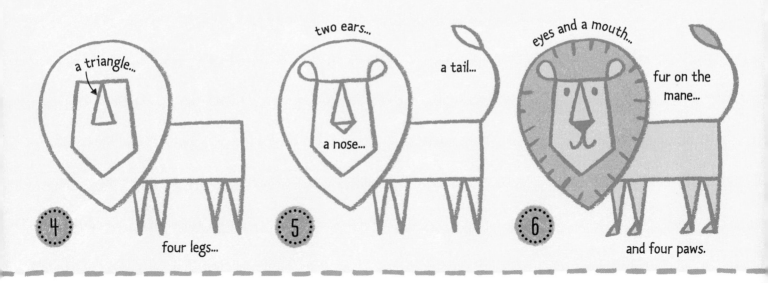

a triangle...

four legs...

two ears...

a nose...

a tail...

eyes and a mouth...

fur on the mane...

and four paws.

Try this...

Female lions don't have manes, so to draw a female lion, skip step 1 and extend the body to meet the head, like this.

How to draw a penguin

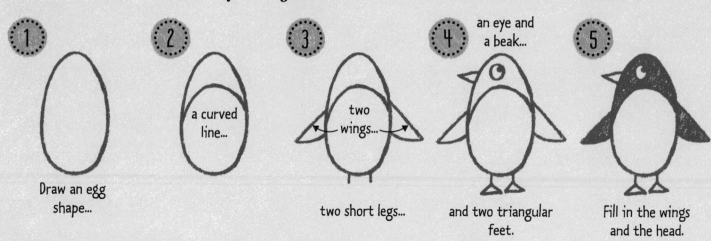

1 Draw an egg shape...

2 a curved line...

3 two wings... two short legs...

4 an eye and a beak... and two triangular feet.

5 Fill in the wings and the head.

Your turn...

Try this...

For a swimming penguin, draw the egg shape at an angle, like this. Bubbles and lines make it look like it's moving through the water.

Draw the wings like this...

a beak...

and add bubbles and water lines.

How to draw an elephant

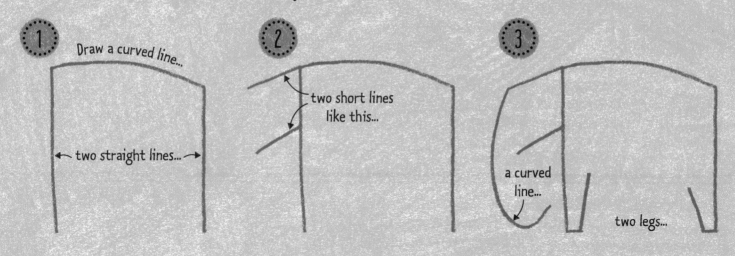

1 Draw a curved line...
← two straight lines... →

2 two short lines like this...

3 a curved line...
two legs...

Your turn...

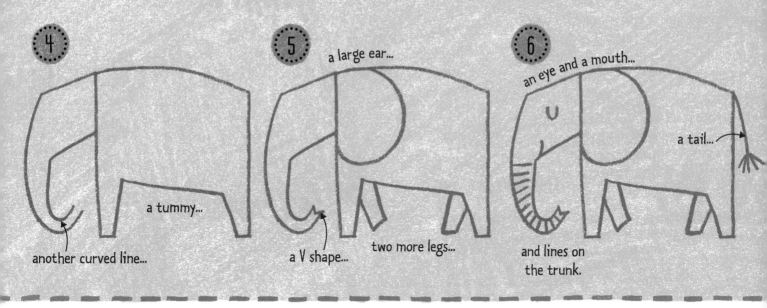

4 another curved line...   a tummy...

5 a large ear...   a V shape...   two more legs...

6 an eye and a mouth...   a tail...   and lines on the trunk.

Try this...

You could add a tusk when you get to step 2.

Draw a tusk here...

then finish in the same way.

How to draw a sloth

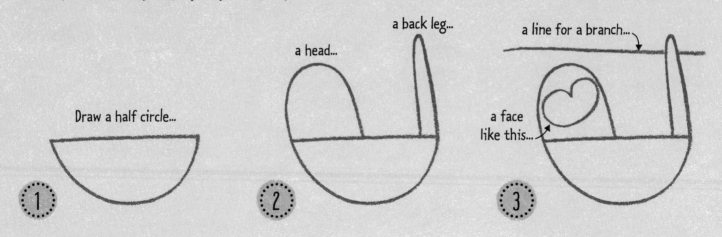

Draw a half circle...

1

a head...

a back leg...

2

a line for a branch...

a face like this...

3

Your turn...

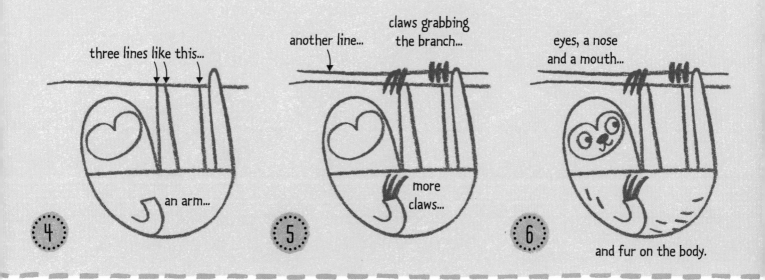

three lines like this...

an arm...

4

another line...

claws grabbing the branch...

more claws...

5

eyes, a nose and a mouth...

and fur on the body.

6

How to draw an ostrich

Your turn...

1 Draw a round head...

2 a body...

3 a long neck...

the tops of its legs...

4 tail feathers...

a curve...

two long legs...

5 an eye and a beak...

a wavy line...

and claws like this.

6 Fill in the body...

and add lines on the legs.

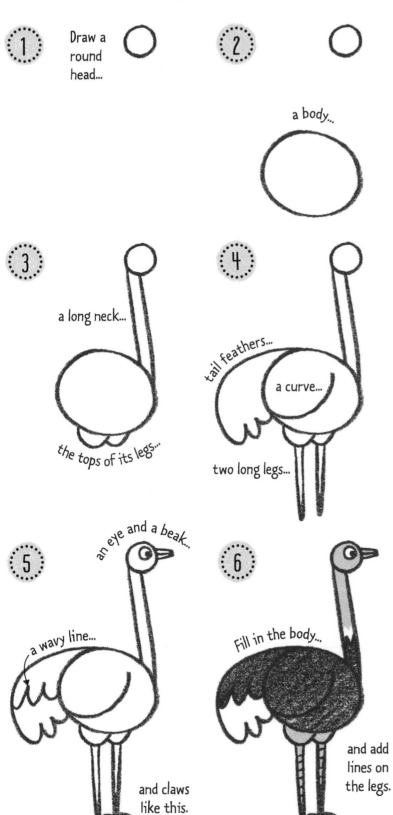

10

Try this...

For a running ostrich, draw the body and head, and make these changes to the neck, legs and tail.

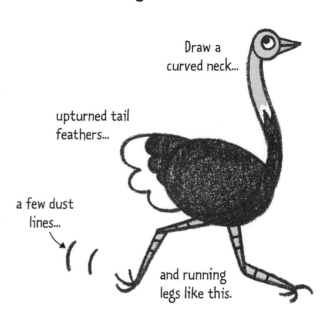

Draw a curved neck...

upturned tail feathers...

a few dust lines...

and running legs like this.

How to draw a zebra

1 Draw an L shape...

2 a head... a curved line... a body...

3 two pointed ears... a nose... a tail... two legs...

Your turn...

an eye...

a mane...

a nostril and
a mouth...

4

a front leg...

another
back leg...

fill in the
nose, mane
and tail...

5

and add lots
of stripes.

6

13

How to draw a meerkat

 Draw a petal-shaped head...

 a long, petal-shaped body...

 two short legs...

 a V shape... a long tail...

 an ear...

another V shape to finish the arms...

two feet...

an eye, a nose and a mouth...

and stripes on its back.

14

How to draw a parrot

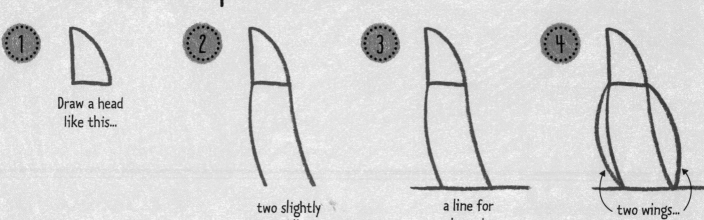

1 Draw a head like this...

2 two slightly curved lines...

3 a line for a branch...

4 two wings...

Your turn...

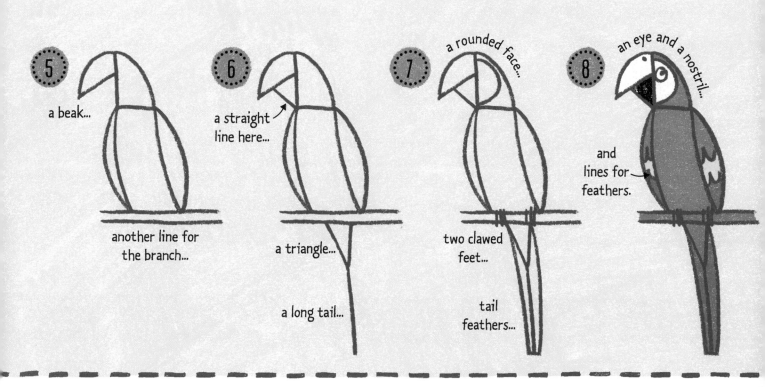

5 a beak...

another line for the branch...

6 a straight line here...

a triangle...

a long tail...

7 a rounded face...

two clawed feet...

tail feathers...

8 an eye and a nostril...

and lines for feathers.

Try this...

The parrot above is a scarlet macaw. Use blue, yellow and green to turn it into a blue-and-gold macaw.

How to draw a tiger

Your turn...

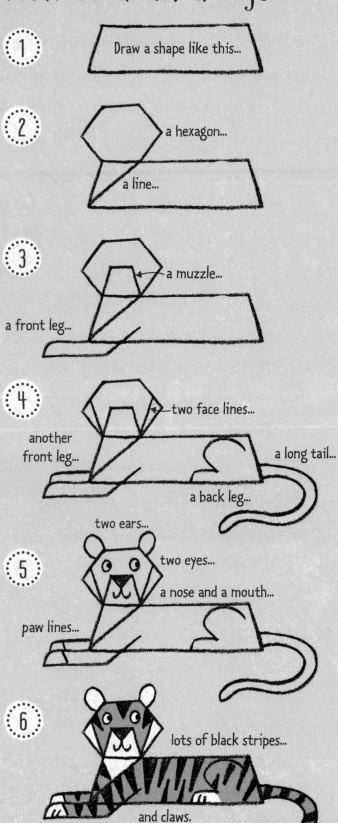

1. Draw a shape like this...

2. a hexagon...
   a line...

3. a muzzle...
   a front leg...

4. two face lines...
   another front leg...
   a long tail...
   a back leg...

5. two ears...
   two eyes...
   a nose and a mouth...
   paw lines...

6. lots of black stripes...
   and claws.

18

How to draw a camel

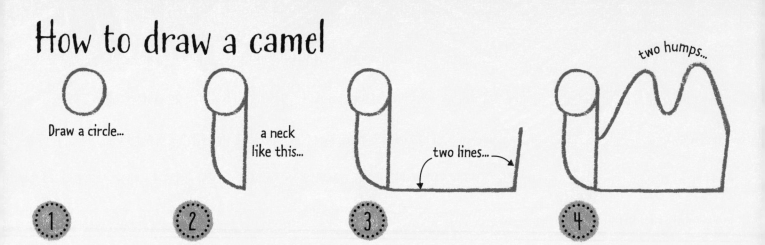

two humps...

Draw a circle...

a neck like this...

two lines...

1

2

3

4

Your turn...

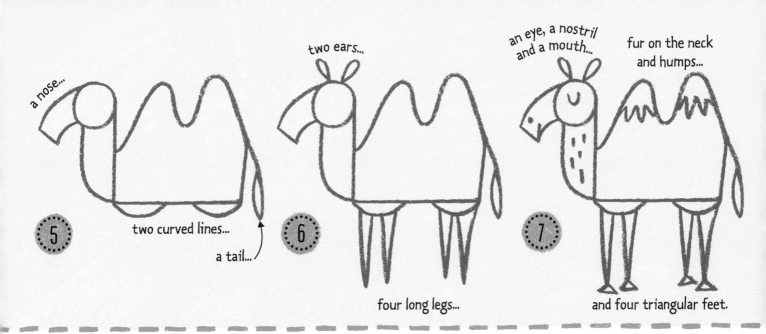

a nose...

two curved lines...

a tail...

5

two ears...

four long legs...

6

an eye, a nostril and a mouth...

fur on the neck and humps...

and four triangular feet.

7

How to draw a monkey

1. Draw a circle...

2. a body...
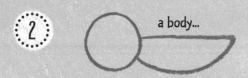

3. two arms... two legs... a long, curled tail...
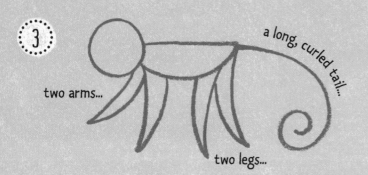

4. a face... two hands... two feet...
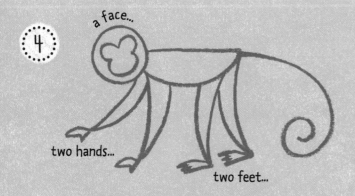

5. two ears... eyes, a nose and a mouth... and fur.
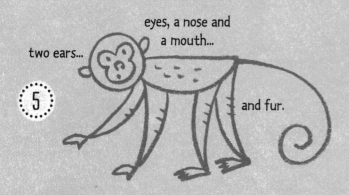

Your turn...

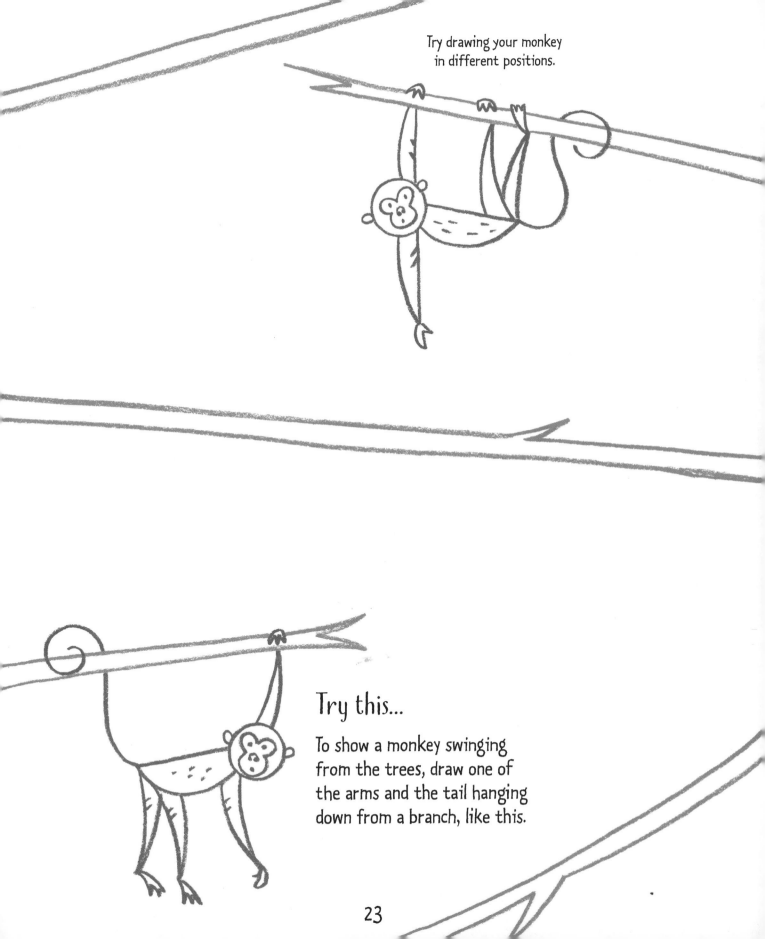

Try drawing your monkey
in different positions.

Try this...

To show a monkey swinging
from the trees, draw one of
the arms and the tail hanging
down from a branch, like this.

How to draw a bald eagle

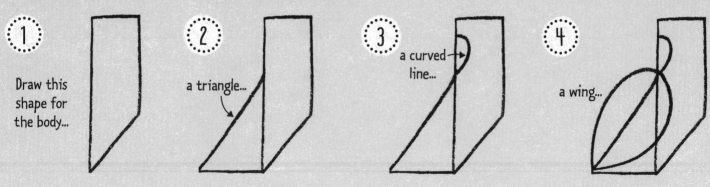

1 Draw this shape for the body...

2 a triangle...

3 a curved line...

4 a wing...

Your turn...

24

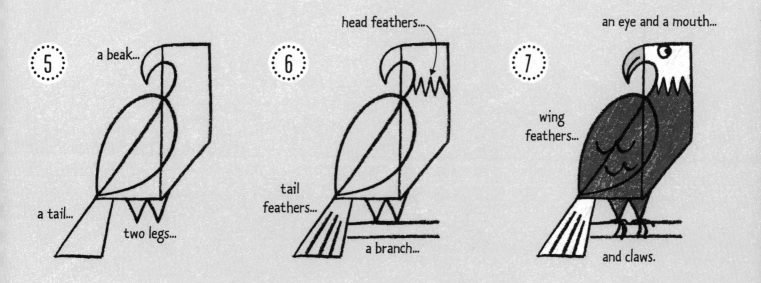

5 a beak...

a tail...

two legs...

6 head feathers....

tail feathers...

a branch...

7 an eye and a mouth...

wing feathers...

and claws.

How to draw a lemur

1 Draw this shape for the head...

2 a triangular body...

3 a long, curved tail...

a triangle...

a smaller triangle...

4 two ears...

two eyes...

a nose...

four legs...

5 a line...

eye lines...

and claws.

6 Add fur and stripes on the tail!

Fill in the areas shown on the face.

Your turn...

How to draw a leopard

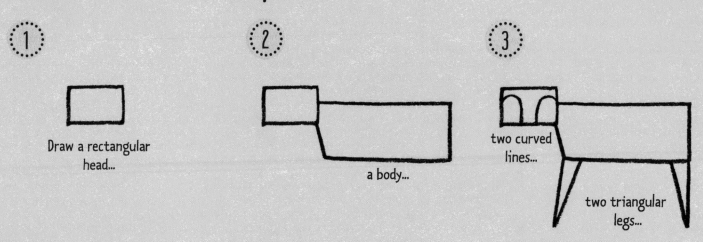

①

Draw a rectangular head...

②

a body...

③

two curved lines...

two triangular legs...

Your turn...

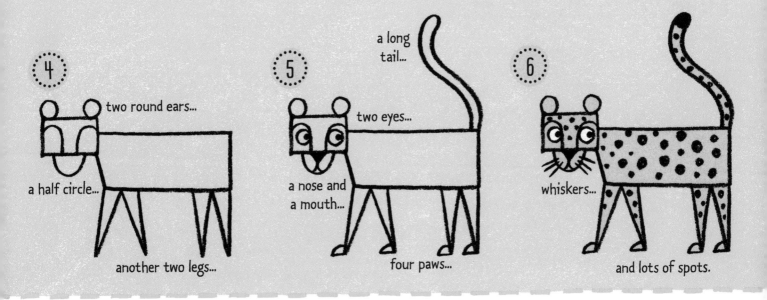

4 two round ears...

a half circle...

another two legs...

5 a long tail...

two eyes...

a nose and a mouth...

four paws...

6 whiskers...

and lots of spots.

How to draw a wolf

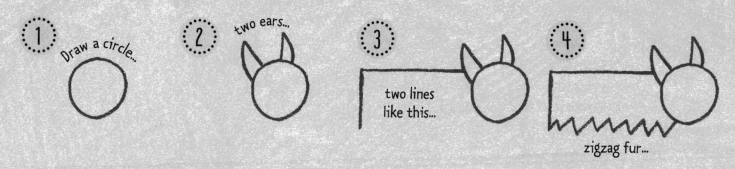

1 Draw a circle...

2 two ears...

3 two lines like this...

4 zigzag fur...

Your turn...

5. a line like this... two legs...

6. a furry tail... another two legs... a muzzle...

7. eyes, a mouth and a nose... and four paws.

31

How to draw a gazelle

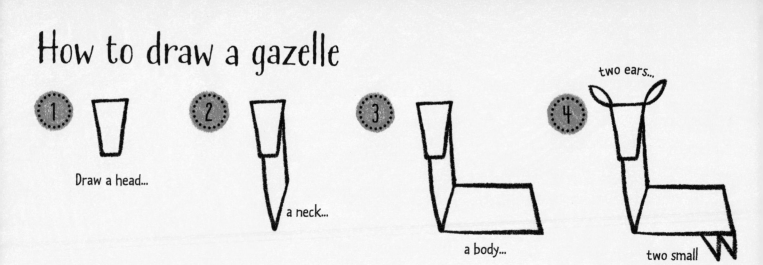

1 Draw a head...

2 a neck...

3 a body...

4 two ears...

two small triangles...

Your turn...

5 two lines on the face...

two front legs...

6 two antlers...

two eyes...

two nostrils...

two back legs...

7 lines on the antlers...

a body stripe...

and a tail.

How to draw a flamingo

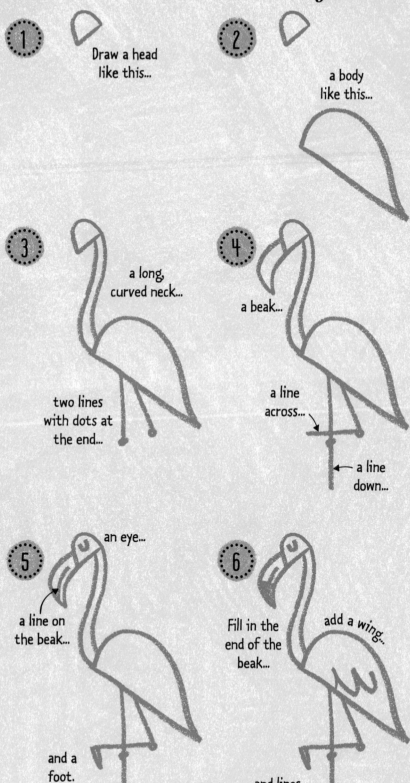

1 Draw a head like this...

2 a body like this...

3 a long, curved neck...

two lines with dots at the end...

4 a beak...

a line across...

a line down...

5 an eye...

a line on the beak...

and a foot.

6 Fill in the end of the beak...

add a wing...

and lines for water.

Try this...

For a flamingo looking for food, turn the body like this. Draw both its legs and its neck reaching down into the water, then add lines for water around them.

How to draw a cheetah

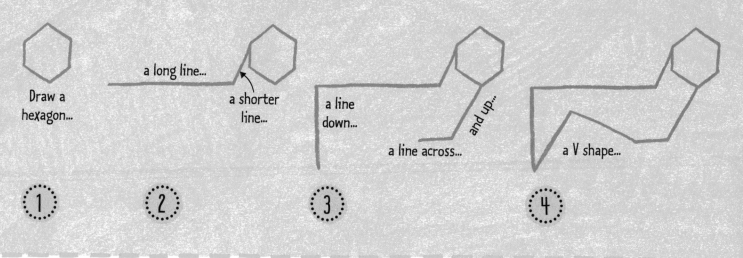

Draw a
hexagon...

a long line...

a shorter
line...

a line
down...

a line across...

and up...

a V shape...

① ② ③ ④

Your turn...

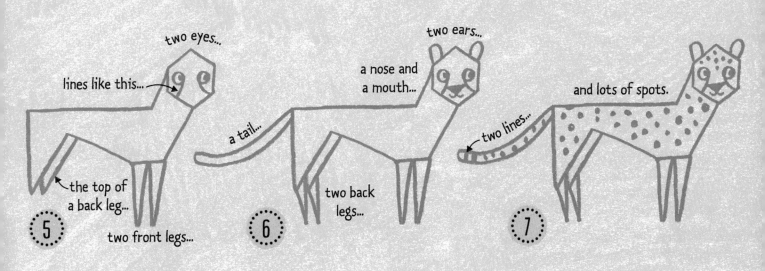

two eyes...

lines like this...

the top of a back leg...

two front legs...

5

a tail...

two back legs...

a nose and a mouth...

two ears...

6

two lines...

and lots of spots.

7

How to draw a cobra

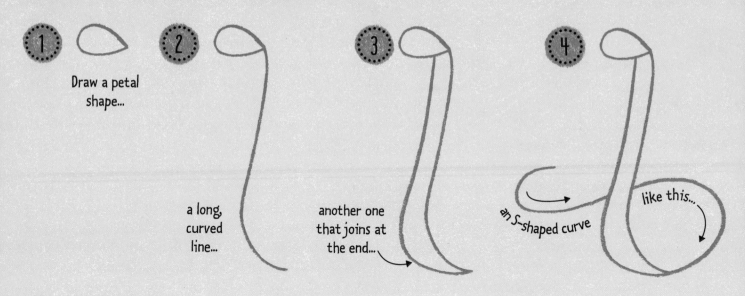

1 Draw a petal shape...

2 a long, curved line...

3 another one that joins at the end...

4 an S-shaped curve   like this...

Your turn...

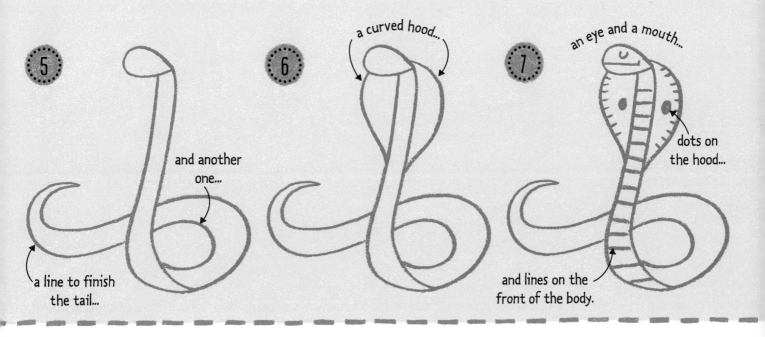

5 a line to finish the tail...

and another one...

6 a curved hood...

7 an eye and a mouth...

dots on the hood...

and lines on the front of the body.

Try this...

For a rattlesnake, draw a petal shape, like this. Leave off the hood, and draw a rattle at the end of the tail. You could add triangles to the body, too.

Draw the head this way around...

and add lines at the end of the tail.

39

How to draw a toucan

Your turn...

1

Draw two
straight lines...

2

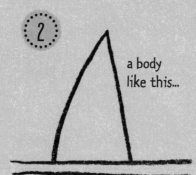

a body
like this...

3

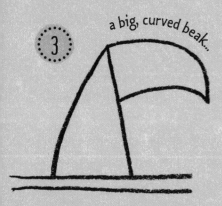

a big, curved beak...

4

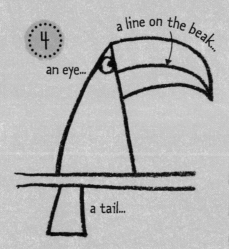

a line on the beak...

an eye...

a tail...

5

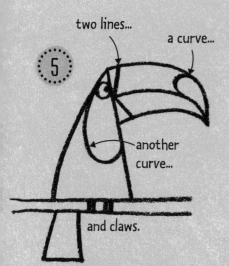

two lines...

a curve...

another
curve...

and claws.

6

Fill in the beak...

the body...

and the tail.

40

How to draw a hippo

1  Draw an oval...

2 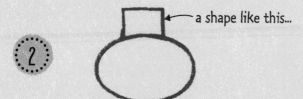 a shape like this...

3 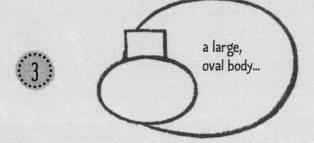 a large, oval body...

4 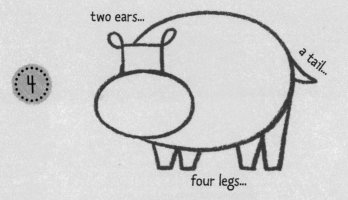 two ears... a tail... four legs...

5  two eyes... spots... nostrils, stubble and a wide mouth.

Your turn...

42

Try this...

For a hippo wallowing in a muddy lake, draw the head like this. Hippos like to keep their bodies cool in the water, so you might only see their head.

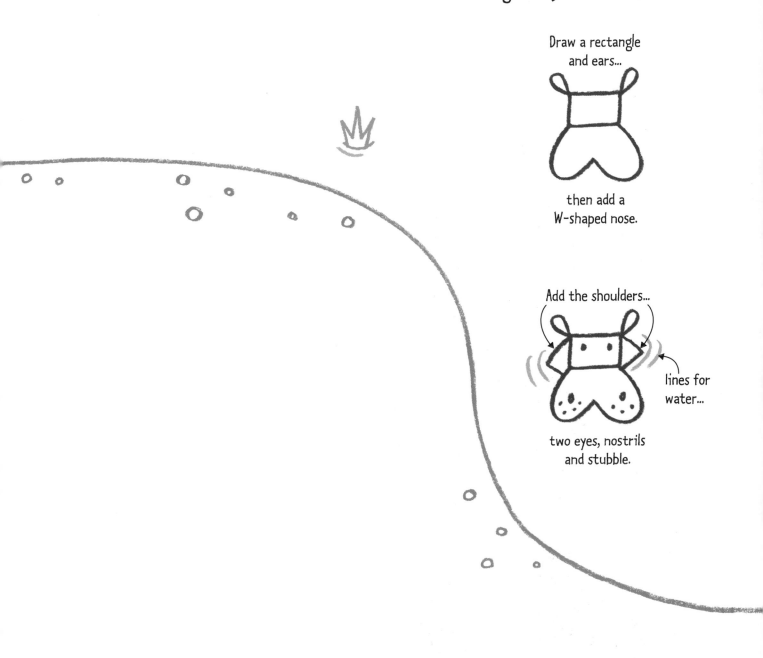

Draw a rectangle and ears...

then add a W-shaped nose.

Add the shoulders...

lines for water...

two eyes, nostrils and stubble.

43

How to draw a tapir

1 Draw an oval body...

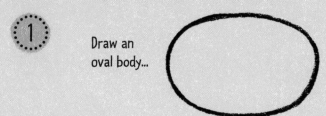

2

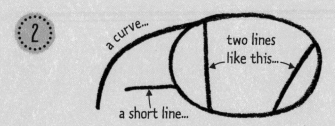

a curve...

two lines like this...

a short line...

3

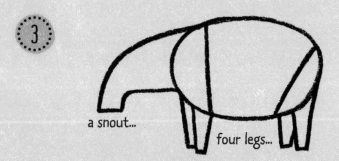

a snout...

four legs...

4

an eye...

two ears...

a tail...

a nostril and a mouth...

and feet.

5

Fill in the body and head.

44

How to draw a panda

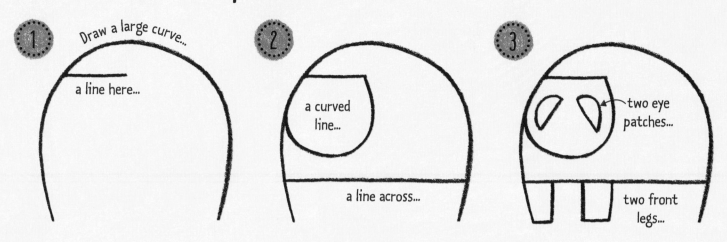

1 Draw a large curve... a line here...

2 a curved line... a line across...

3 two eye patches... two front legs...

Your turn...

4 a curved line...

two back legs...

5 ears, eyes, a nose and a mouth.

6 Fill these areas in black.

Try this...

You can use the basic shape of the panda to draw a brown bear, too. When you get to step 2, change your drawing like this. Follow the instructions to finish the bear's face and body.

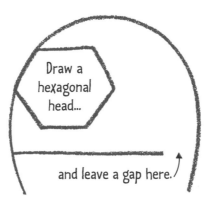

Draw a hexagonal head...

and leave a gap here.

Add two lines for the muzzle...

shapes inside the ears...

and lines for fur.

How to draw an orangutan

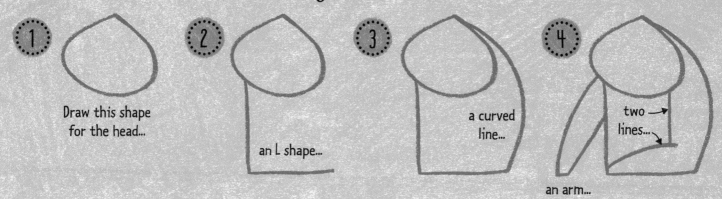

1. Draw this shape for the head...

2. an L shape...

3. a curved line...

4. two → lines...

an arm...

Your turn...

48

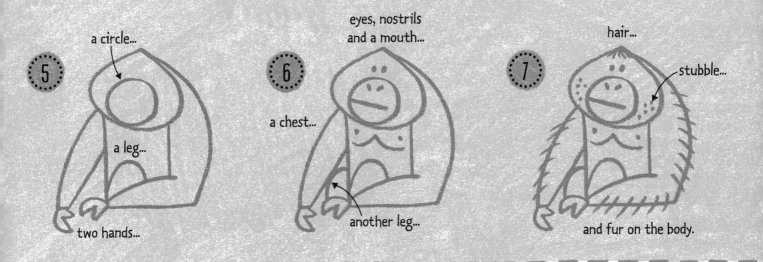

5 a circle...
a leg...
two hands...

6 eyes, nostrils and a mouth...
a chest...
another leg...

7 hair...
stubble...
and fur on the body.

How to draw a tortoise

1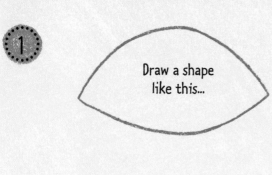
Draw a shape like this...

2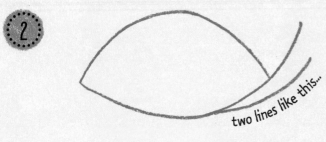
two lines like this...

3
a head...

4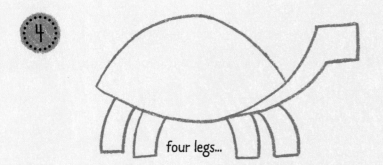
four legs...

5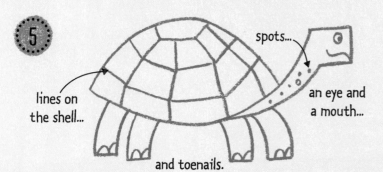
spots...
lines on the shell...
an eye and a mouth...
and toenails.

How to draw a tamarin monkey

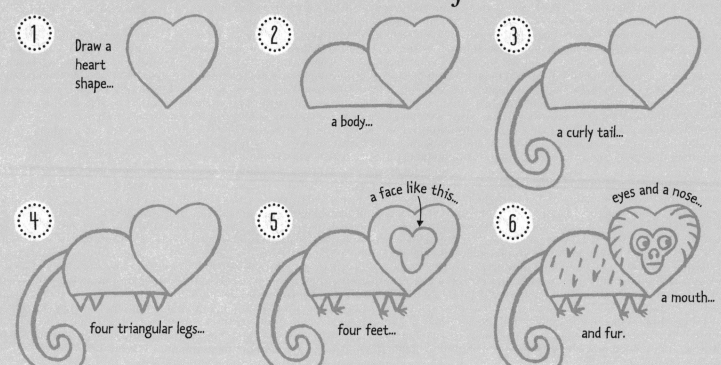

1. Draw a heart shape...

2. a body...

3. a curly tail...

4. four triangular legs...

5. a face like this... four feet...

6. eyes and a nose... a mouth... and fur.

Your turn...

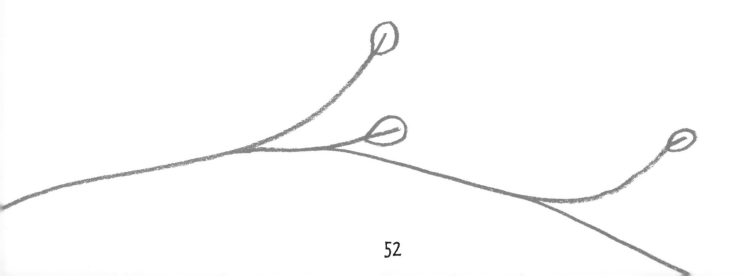

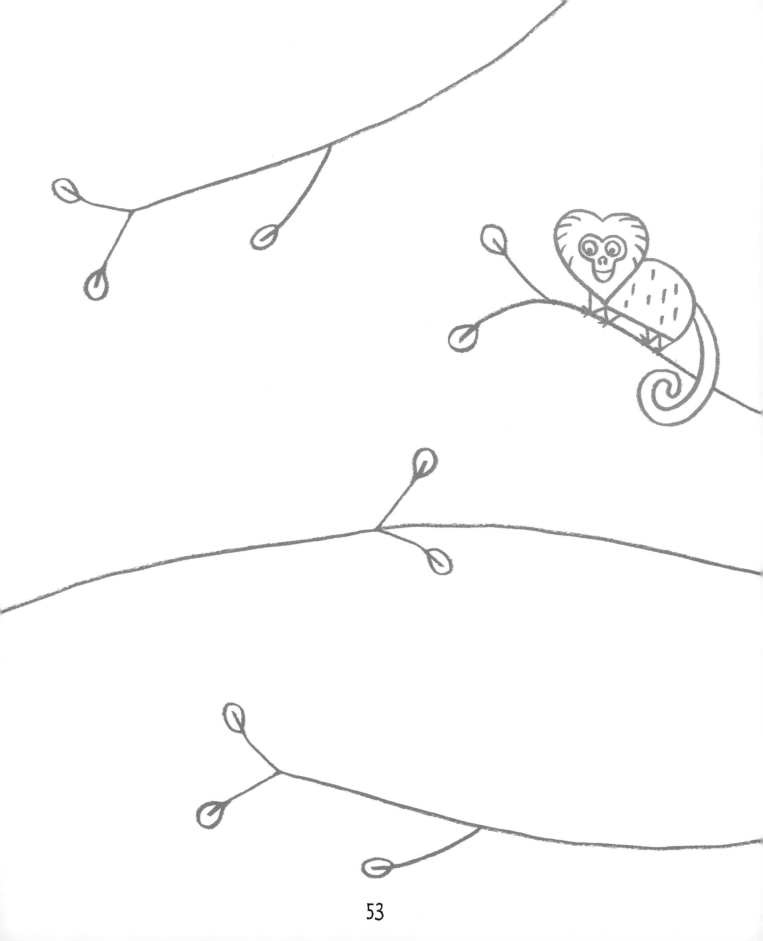

How to draw a kangaroo

1. Draw an oval...

2. a line...

3. a curved back leg...

Your turn...

4

a head...

a foot...

5

two pointed ears...

a long, thick tail...

an arm...

6

an eye, a nose and a mouth...

and a front paw.

Try this...

For a baby kangaroo (a joey), draw one much smaller. You could draw a joey looking out of its mother's pouch.

Draw a little head, like this. →

How to draw a lizard

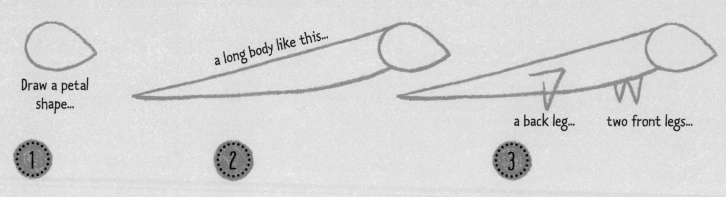

1 Draw a petal shape...

2 a long body like this...

3 a back leg... two front legs...

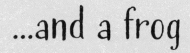

Your turn...

...and a frog

1 Draw a leaf shape...

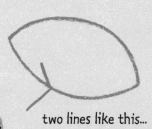

2 two lines like this...

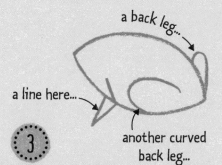

a back leg...

a line here...

3 another curved back leg...

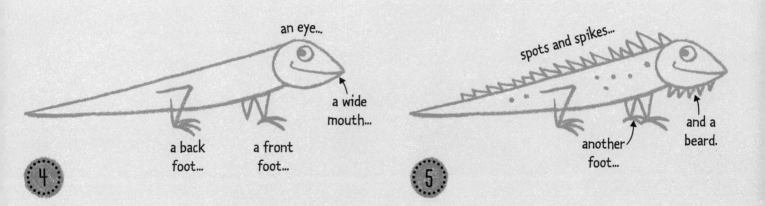

4
an eye...
a wide
mouth...
a back
foot...
a front
foot...

5
spots and spikes...
another
foot...
and a
beard.

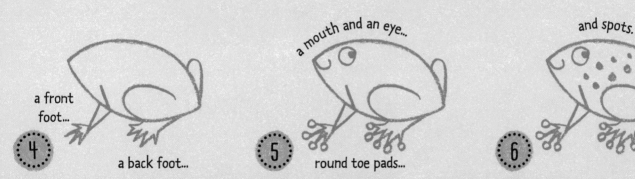

4
a front
foot...
a back foot...

5
a mouth and an eye...
round toe pads...

6
and spots.

57

How to draw a hyena

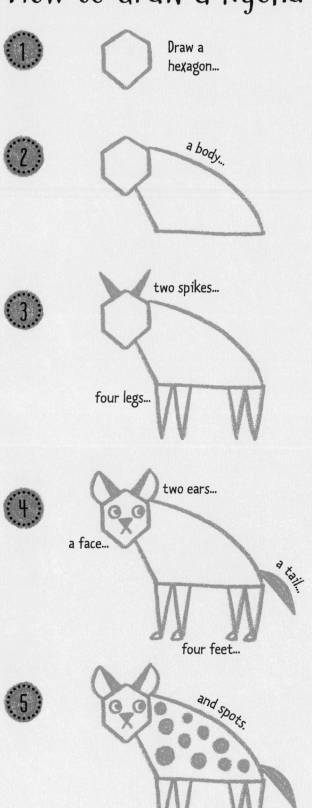

1 Draw a hexagon...

2 a body...

3 two spikes...
four legs...

4 two ears...
a face...
a tail...
four feet...

5 and spots.

Your turn...

How to draw a koala

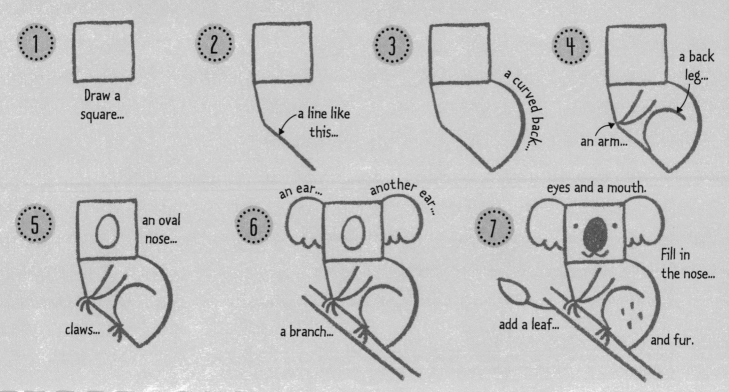

1 Draw a square...

2 a line like this...

3 a curved back...

4 a back leg... an arm...

5 an oval nose... claws...

6 an ear... another ear... a branch...

7 eyes and a mouth. Fill in the nose... add a leaf... and fur.

Your turn...

How to draw a rhino

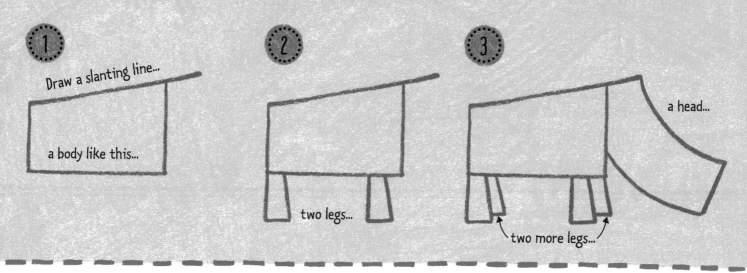

1 Draw a slanting line... a body like this...

2 two legs...

3 two more legs... a head...

Your turn...

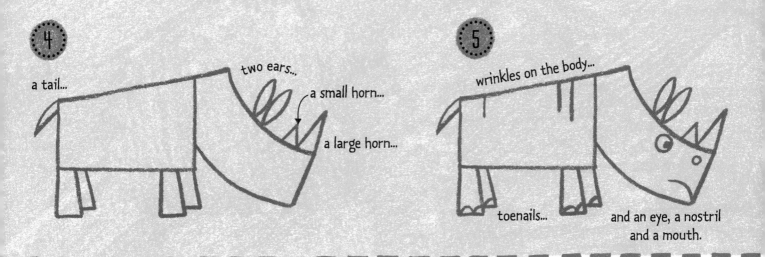

4

a tail...

two ears...

a small horn...

a large horn...

5

wrinkles on the body...

toenails...

and an eye, a nostril
and a mouth.

How to draw a chameleon

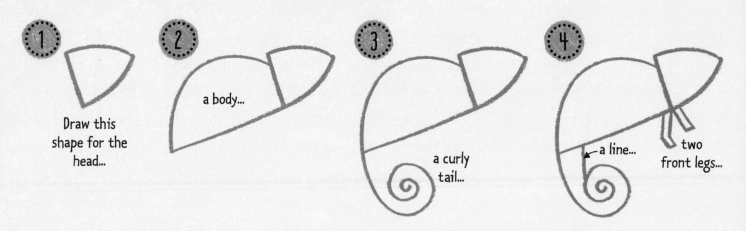

1 Draw this shape for the head...

2 a body...

3 a curly tail...

4 a line... two front legs...

Your turn...

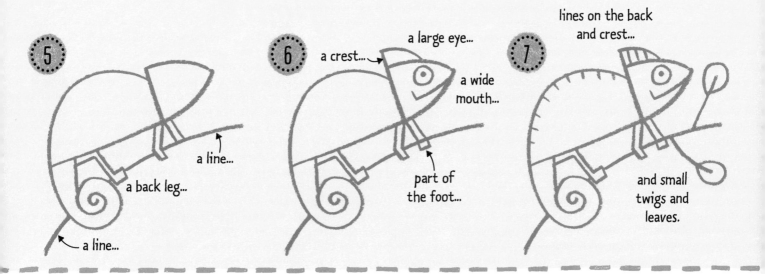

5 a line...

a back leg...

a line...

6 a crest...

a large eye...

a wide mouth...

part of the foot...

7 lines on the back and crest...

and small twigs and leaves.

How to draw a crocodile

Your turn...

1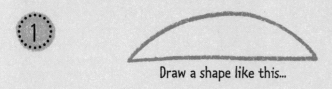

Draw a shape like this...

2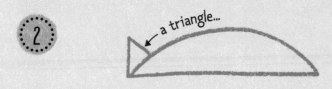

a triangle...

3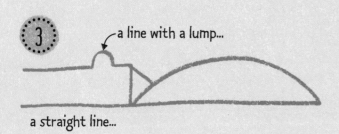

a line with a lump...

a straight line...

4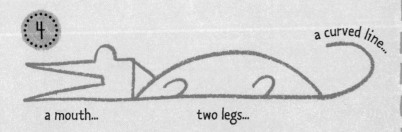

a curved line...

a mouth...   two legs...

5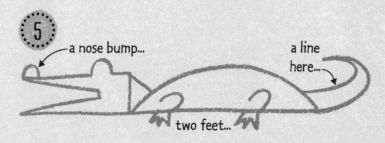

a nose bump...   a line here...

two feet...

6

a nostril and an eye...

and spots on the body.

sharp teeth...

66

Try this...

For a swimming crocodile, don't add the legs or tail. Draw lines for water around the body instead. You could also draw the mouth closed, like this.

How to draw a gorilla

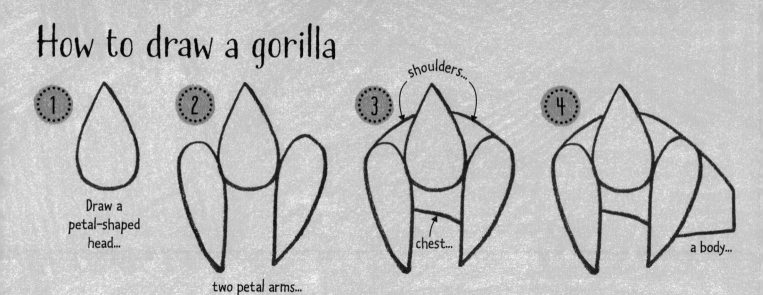

1 Draw a petal-shaped head...

2 two petal arms...

3 shoulders... chest...

4 a body...

Your turn...

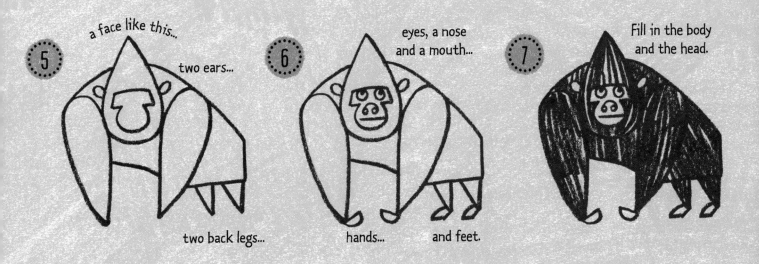

5 a face like this...
two ears...
two back legs...

6 eyes, a nose and a mouth...
hands...
and feet.

7 Fill in the body and the head.

How to draw a wildebeest

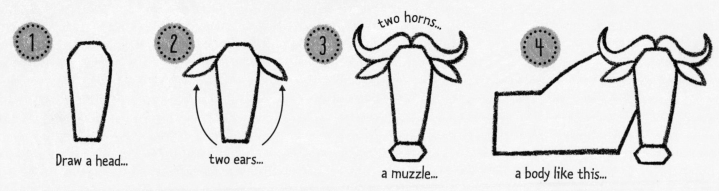

1 Draw a head...

2 two ears...

3 two horns... a muzzle...

4 a body like this...

Your turn...

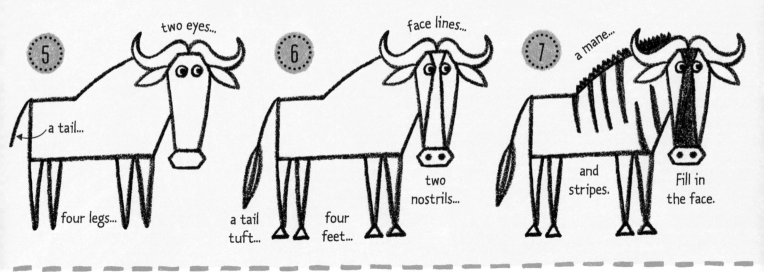

5 two eyes...

a tail...

four legs...

6 face lines...

a tail tuft...

four feet...

two nostrils...

7 a mane...

and stripes.

Fill in the face.

How to draw a giraffe

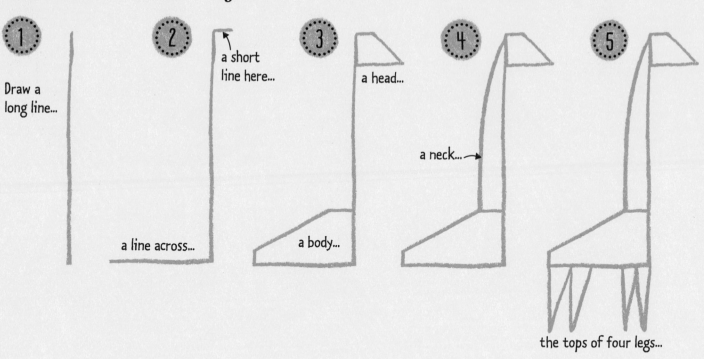

1 Draw a long line... a line across...

2 a short line here... a line across...

3 a head... a body...

4 a head... a neck...

5 a head... the tops of four legs...

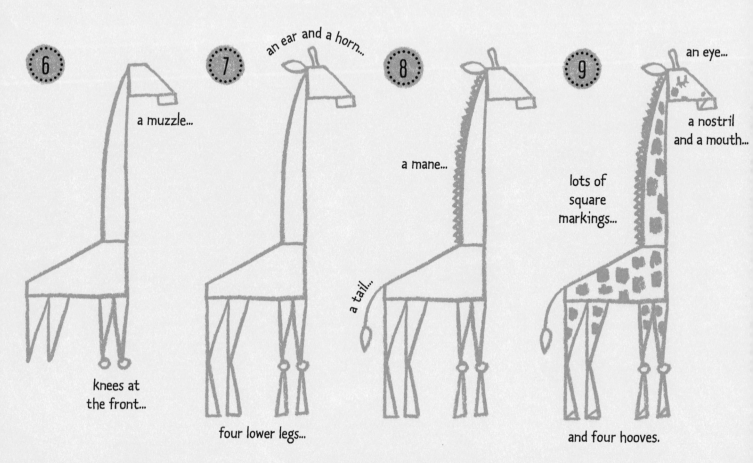

6 a muzzle... knees at the front...

7 an ear and a horn... four lower legs...

8 a mane... a tail...

9 an eye... a nostril and a mouth... lots of square markings... and four hooves.

Your turn...

How to draw a chimpanzee

Draw a circle...

an oval...

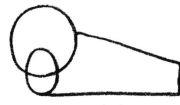

a body...

a face like this...

 1

2

3

4

Your turn...

74

5 four legs...

6 two ears...
two hands... two feet...

7 eyes and nostrils.
Fill in the fur.

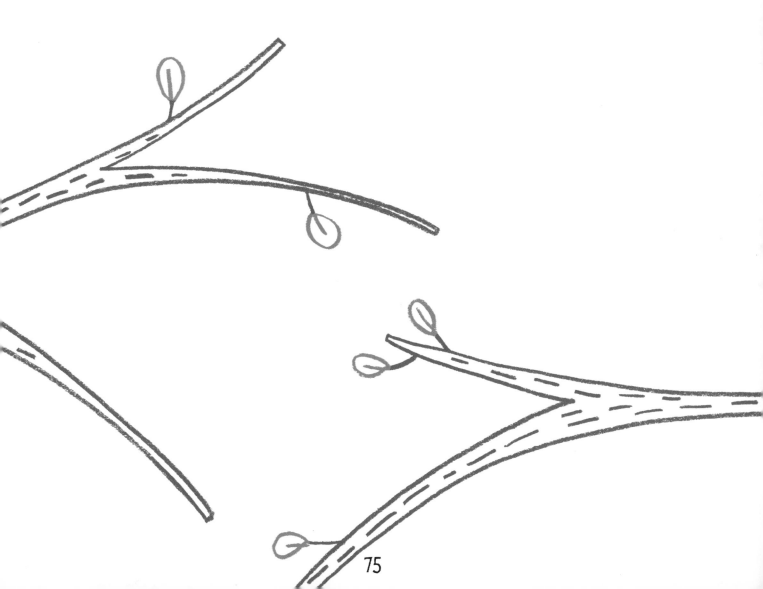

A day at the zoo

The following pages have ideas for scenes created from pictures in the book. Use the ideas to finish drawing the scenes, and fill them in with pens or pencils.

Draw more penguins in the pool.

Draw a gorilla family.

TICKETS

Add some visitors walking around.

76

LEMURS

Draw more hippos
taking a swim.

GORILLAS | HIPPOS

Add railings to the
hippo enclosure.

Draw a female lion lying down.

Add more bones.

At the safari park

Draw a herd
of zebra.

Add more bushes.

This camel has
two friends.

Add more rhinos.

Add more cars on the road.

Add some trees.

Draw a baby giraffe.

Tropical house

Toucans love this spot.

Draw another macaw perching on a branch.

Add more branches and tropical flowers.

Draw another flamingo.

Add another chameleon or a lizard.